Mining and Quarrying
in the
Teign Valley

by

STAFFORD CLARK

I wish to thank Mary for her patience and forebearance, and my family Susan, Stephen and Edward for their help given to me whilst writing this book.

Photography - Alan Pebworth and Stafford Clark

First published in Great Britain in 1995

Published by ORCHARD PUBLICATIONS
2 Orchard Close, Chudleigh, Newton Abbot, Devon. TQ13 0LR
Telephone: (01626) 852714

ISBN 1 898964 19 X

Designed, Typeset and Printed for Orchard Publications by
Swift Print
Dawlish
Devon EX7 9HP

INDEX

INTRODUCTION

The course of the Teign River is described in a 1922 touring guide as follows:-
"after leaving the neighbourhood of Sittaford Tor and the Grey Wethers, the river flows first north and then east and north-east for some distance and bending to the south at Dunsford makes its way into its estuary". The peaceful appearance of the wooded valley today conceals a surprisingly rich legacy from its industrial past, an era of productive mining and quarrying, spanning many generations, some of which still operate today. It is a history of mineral extraction so rich and varied in nature which had such a dramatic impact upon the scenery and character of the valley that it is worth a detailed exploration. This book sets out to do that, following the river from its rising in the moors to its estuary at Teignmouth.

Tin, lead, silver, barytes, manganese and copper were among the many minerals extracted from the valley, as well as the high quality stone granite, limestone and basalt, all quarried in the area. Finally there are vast deposits of ball-clay in the Bovey Basin. It is not surprising that when, during the early post-war years, a DC3 Dakota aircraft flew regularly up and down the valley trailing a strange device, a blob on the end of a cable hanging almost 100ft below its body, the general consensus of the valley residents, used to such wealth beneath the ground was, "They'm lookin ver Uranium".

A GEOLOGICAL PICTURE OF THE AREA

The middle Teign Valley, which lies between the high ground of north-eastern Dartmoor and the ridge of Great Haldon, is an area of considerable geological complexity. Much of the area between Dunsford and Chudleigh Knighton is underlain by rocks of Late Devonian to Early Carboniferous age including slate, shale and chert (bedded siliceous rock not unlike flint), together with volcanic strata, such as spilite (submarine lavas) and tuff (lithified volcanic ash). All of these rocks have been caught up in movements deep in the Earth's crust, so that they have been folded and fractured; when in the district we see beds of these rocks in quarries or roadside cuttings, they are commonly inclined at steep angles and are cut by closely spaced joints and fractures. To the west lies the Dartmoor Granite, which was injected into the folded slates and shales as molten magma about 280 million years ago, afterwards cooling to form the characteristic crystalline granite. The heat from this event locally baked the rocks immediately adjacent to the granite causing them to become extremely hard and tough: these rocks of the 'metamorphic aureole' extend in an arc from Drewsteignton through Bridford to Hennock. To the east of the Teign, the older folded rocks are overlain by younger underformed strata of the Permian red beds and the Greensand of Haldon ridge. In places, the older rocks, both granite and slate are cut by fractures that have been filled by mineral deposits, the result of the passage through the rocks of metal-bearing solutions. This has resulted in the development of haematite (iron oxide) veins in the area between Hennock and Lustleigh, and of a major, north-south trending complex of veins between Bridford and Teign Village that has yielded substantial quantities of lead, silver and barite (barium sulphate) together with minor amounts of zinc, copper, fluorspar and iron ore. Small amounts of manganese ores have been worked from bedded deposits within the Carboniferous cherts and volcanic strata.

R C Scrivener BSc PhD FGS.
1995

A PRECAUTIONARY NOTE

Old mine and quarry workings are obviously areas of great interest, but they are also places of considerable danger. Many of the workings mentioned in this book are on private land and not accessible to the general public. However, real enthusiasts may be granted limited access if permission is requested from the owners. Whether exploring old sites on private or public land, please exercise great caution.

MAPS AND GRID REFERENCES

MAPS

For any reader wishing to use this book as an exploration of the mining and quarrying activities in the Teign Valley then the following Ordnance Survey maps will be extremely helpful.
Pathfinder 1328 SX 68/78
Pathfinder 1329 SX 88/98
Pathfinder 1342 SX 87/97
Outdoor Leisure No. 28 (also covering Pathfinder 1329)
All these maps are 1 : 25.000 Scale *(2¹/₄ inches to 1 mile)*

GRID REFERENCES

A grid reference is used to locate a certain area on an Ordnance Survey map. Grid References used in this book contain six numbers e.g. 784-859. To identify this reference take your map and working from left to right (west to east) find the vertical grid line showing the first two numbers (78). The top line of the map is broken into one-tenth markings and using this line find the fourth such marking - hence you now have a reference of 784.
Use the same method for the second set of three figures, but this time working up from the bottom of the map until you find the horizontal line 85. Find the final number (9) as before by counting off the one-tenth markings, and by using a ruler or a good eye find where the vertical and horizontal lines meet - in this example Blackingstone Quarry 784-859.

CHAGFORD - A STANNARY TOWN

To the north west of the town, the North and South Teign rivers rise out of bogs and catchment areas of north-east Dartmoor, and it was in this wild windswept region that men streamed for tin. They used the prolific water supplies after heavy rains to scour the man-made gullies or ditches excavated just for that purpose, the peat and sparse soil piled high on each side. Leats were later dug bringing water from the moorland streams to give a more constant supply. Inevitably tin brought a measure of prosperity to the town and eventually it became an important trade centre with its own market. Chagford or 'Chaggyford', is described in the 1922 touring guide mentioned in the introduction as an old market and stannary town where "all tastes can be gratified, fishing, golfing, antiquaries, and lovers of scenery. The town was one of the first to have electric light".

Such was the importance of this metal that Edward 1 gave permission for Stannators to be chosen to attend the Tinner's Parliament at Crockern Tor, and their first meeting was held on the windswept tor in 1494. Of the four stannary towns, Chagford lies well to the east of the tor, not a pleasant walk in extreme weather. A Tinner's Guild was later set up in Chagford, its patron being St. Katherine.

The tin, after smelting at the various blowing houses, would require transport to its collecting point. This is where the pack-horses played their part passing down the valley, collecting tin from other sites below the town, almost as far as Fingle. Here they crossed the river by fording it, and later in the 16th century, by its stone bridge. The River Teign after heavy rainfall rises quickly and conversely soon falls.

Before the discovery of tin in the area around Chagford, agriculture would have been the basic industry, even as far as the estuary. This continued to be the main occupation of the valley population, with its attendant services of blacksmith, cobbler, mason, carpenter, wheelwright, baker, miller etc, until the end of the 18th century. In Chagford itself, there was a thriving 'Serge and Blanket Manufactory', as recorded in 1871, run by John Vicary, and four mills were busy processing corn products.

However, it was tin that the prosperity of Chagford was founded upon, and it would seem that some areas of Devon were as well blessed in that valuable metal as its western neighbour, Cornwall. It is interesting to consider what might have been the eventual outcome if, under the Act of Parliament of 1883, the Exeter, Teign Valley and Chagford Railway had been fully constructed with possible stations at Dunsford, Fingle (serving Drewsteignton) and Sandygate, terminating at Chagford, then called the 'Torquay of the Moors'. The use of the line for heavy goods trains could have encouraged further exploration for tin, perhaps the opening of deep mines, another quarry for limestone or even granite.

4

The following Ordnance Survey Grid References show the positions of excavated areas around Chagford, probably involved with the tin streaming:

Approx:	600yds S.W. of Great Weeke
	GR. 712-874

Approx:	500yds S.W. of Westcott
	GR. 708-874

The will of a John Westcott, 1522, refers to tin streaming at Dogamarsh, and records also refer to this method of obtaining tin from Higher Liners Beam and Chagford Common.

The majority of the older houses and buildings in Chagford have been built of granite, most of which was probably taken and cut from the nearby surface stones of Nattadon and Meldon Common.
Sites of stone quarries:

Approx:	600yds E of Nattadon Road.
	GR. 703-869

Approx:	300yds E of Meldon Hill
	GR. 700-866

Approx:	1/4 mile W of 'Hole'
	GR. 689-860

DREWSTEIGNTON - BLACK ALLER QUARRY

On a prominent site high above the river stands Castle Drogo, a 20th century castle built in Dartmoor granite and dominating the well-known Fingle Gorge, as described by R.D. Blackmore:-

> *"It is the finest thing to look at in the West of England. As in the vales of Lyn or Barle the rugged lines of Exmoor descend in grace, so here, the sterner heights and strengths of Dartmoor fall with beauty and yet preserve their grandeur".*

High on the western side, Cranbrook Castle, an ancient hill fortress, overlooks the other hill forts of Prestonbury on the east bank and Wooston Castle. Drewsteignton, the name is derived from its 20th century owner Drew or Drogo, is situated across the gorge from Cranbook. Its houses surround a square dominated by the church. A road running south-east falls quickly into the Teign Gorge to where the ancient pack-horse bridge crosses the river.

Black Aller quarry lies approximately half a mile due west from the village and limestone was first extracted from this site in the latter part of the 19th century. The British Geological Survey describes this stone as carboniferous limestone, normally mid-grey with bands of black mineral chert. Limestone is stratified and was usually quarried by first cleaning the topping or overburden, thus exposing the stone. Having marked off an area in block form, holes are pricked at short intervals into which steel wedges are driven until the mass is split right through the stratum. This method produced excellent building face stones of varied size. As demand grew, pneumatic drilling and blasting had to be carried out resulting in much less selectable samples for wall building.

The high grade stone extracted from the Black Aller Quarry formed the basis of the roads in the district and the aggregates from the crushers were used in various ways by builders within a wide radius. There are several buildings in the area whose walls are composed of selected facing stone from the quarry. The full extraction area covered over 20 acres and included two large pits, one of which filled with water in 1909. The limestone strata slopes at about 40° into the huge pit and is a very dangerous area. Lime kilns are still visible, but in a crumbling, ivy-covered state.

Limestone for kilning would have been hauled to the kilns and tipped into the 'burning pit', together with a generous supply of coal, charcoal or dried peat. Later in the 18th century the charcoal and peat were replaced entirely by coal. Firing took place at a great heat. After many hours the fire gradually diminished and eventually died out. Two days later the kiln would be emptied and selected stones bagged and delivered to the merchants.

A building company using the product at the turn of the century would closely inspect each sackful for decomposing stones due to dampness, then using a wooden cask cut in half, of 2ft 6inches minimum diameter, the dry stones would be tipped into it, slowly adding water. As the dry stones absorbed the moisture great heat was generated and the mixture would give off clouds of steam. Slowly more water would be added until the stones were covered, then boiling would take place similar to a saucepan of porridge on a hot stove.

If the 'putty lime' was eventually required for colouring a wall, two cups of tallow would need to be added before boiling commenced and if a creamy coloured exterior wall was required, two eggcups of yellow ochre would be added with the tallow. After cooling the mixture should have the texture of soft cream and was now ready for mortar or wall colouring. The author can recall seeing the boiling process take place as a young boy. The Ley Arms at Kennford was treated with real putty lime wash, in about 1970. Mortar in pre-eighteenth century walls was composed of putty-lime, fine shale or shillit, riversand and small chippings.

In the account books of Samuel Clark of Christow, local builder and the author's grandfather, there are many details of 'hogsheads' of lime for use in 'white-washing' shippens, kitchens, sitting rooms, passages and even the large drawing room at Ashton Manor in 1900. However, from 1914 onwards other decorating materials were available. A 'hogshead' was a statutory liquid measure fixed in 1423, equivalent to 52½ imperial gallons. It was usually a cask whose capacity varied with the commodity. The measurement was later used for cider.

Lias lime, also called Blue Lias, was extensively used in the building industry. Each delivery in one hundredweight (112 lbs) sacks had to be used reasonably quickly, particularly in damp seasons, mixing by hand being the best method.

Seven barrows of sand were deposited in a heap, the whole sack of Lias was then added and the mixing began. As each portion was turned small amounts of water were sprinkled. After many complete turnings the mixture formed a large mound which was covered and left overnight. During this period great heat was generated in the heap, eventually forming a friable lime mortar when a small amount of cement was added. Any mixing not correctly carried out was referred to as 'idle Jack muck' by the masons. Lias lime was used for mortar up until the 1960s when hydrated lime came on the market.

Lying so close to the village of Drewsteignton, the quarry naturally attracted local men who found employment there. Possibly all the lime used in the mortar mixes for the building of nearby Castle Drogo was fired in the old kilns, and undoubtedly there would have been full employment for quite a number of men.

7

Mr. Roger Chudley, a foreman at the quarry with many years service, can recall as many as 25 men engaged in the operations. High on the south side of the narrow approach road was the site of several cottages once occupied by the quarry workers and known as Kiln Village.

Mr. Harold Partridge, the quarry's former owner, handed the business to his son, Alan Partridge, whose wife, upon his death managed the firm until the whole enterprise was sold to Bardon Roadstone Ltd. Sadly the new company decided to close down in 1991 causing hardship to many local families.

The site is within the Park's boundary and its future use is now in the hands of the Dartmoor National Park Committee.

Old Lime Kilns at Black Aller Quarry.

BLACKINGSTONE GRANITE QUARRY (BLACKENSTONE)

A couple of miles south-west of the river sits the massive Blackingstone Rock, a well-known landmark of loaf-shaped granite. Granite is an igneous rock cooled at depth in the earth's crust. A typical cross-section displays cream coloured crystals of Feldspar, rectangular in shape, maybe as large as 75mm, together with Quartz, Mica and Biolite. The name derived from an early Italian word Granito (grained). The quarry GR. 784-858 lies roughly ¾ mile north-west of the Rock and it was from here that stone was cut for the building of Castle Drogo at the beginning of this century. Samuel Clark, a stone mason by trade, worked for some time cutting and shaping pieces for the Castle.

It is easy to imagine the shire horses and heavily laden waggons crossing Mardon Down, passing the ancient earthworks of Canbrook Castle and eventually negotiating the steep hill into the river valley and thence to the extensive building in the course of erection at Drogo.

The quarry face is about 600 feet long and approximately 100 feet high. There is little overburden and it appears to have an abundance of sound, clean stone. There are remains of buildings and smiths' forges, one of which is primitive. The slabs of granite were split out by the use of drive pins or 'gads' roughly every 9-12 inches and as these were slowly driven in, the fractures ran lengthwise; when the break came long slabs resulted.

There are several tips of rejected granite on the north side of the quarry, some are the result of flaws and others have surface discolouration caused by vegetation.

The former owners, Messrs. Eastons, were stone masons whose yards occupied premises on the south side of Lower Northenhay Street, Exeter. During the 1960s the quarry was acquired by Harleyford Aggregates (Messrs. Folley Bros.)

The present owner wishes to continue the operation on a small scale and awaits the result of a planning application lodged with the Dartmoor National Park.

Many local men worked at the quarry, among them Rex Hannaford who although now living in Dawlish, South Devon, worked at Blackingstone between 1940-1965, whilst living in Moretonhampstead. Rex joined his father, Sam Hannaford, who was the general foreman, having worked there since the 1920s. Sam, like the aforementioned Samuel Clark was a master stone mason and was also engaged on the building of Castle Drogo. He moved to the Blackingstone Quarry having learnt his trade at the Merrivale Quarry on the opposite side of the moor. He was the mason responsible for the War Memorial which stands in the churchyard at Sidmouth. The cross bearing the names of those lost in the First World War standing in Budleigh Salterton was also his work, and the base stone bearing the names of those lost in the Second World, which supports the cross, was the work of his son Rex.

Rex recalls a workforce of between six to twelve men working at the quarry whilst he was there and other names remembered are Alf Huxtable the Quarry Foreman; Cecil Dodd, another mason; the blacksmith Herbert Doney whose duties included keeping the working tools in good order. This included welding steel bits into iron bars used as 'jumpers' to bore the holes into the granite prior to the insertion of the 'feathers' or 'gads' to split the granite open. George Clapp was another quarryman, and Moretonhampstead resident Clarence Colwell, who though not a quarry employee, was a jobbing builder who remembers undertaking several jobs at Blackingstone on the quarry buildings and offices whilst it was in operation.

The use of Black powder was the means of blasting or lifting the granite, and Rex recalls with some humour how the new owners, upon Eastons selling the quarry, tried using dynamite and gelignite. This resulted in showering the countryside for several hundred yards around with lumps and shafts of stone of all shapes and sizes. When blasting was about to take place all the employees made sure they were well out of the way. Black powder was soon re-instated as the blasting component.

Blackingstone Rock.

10

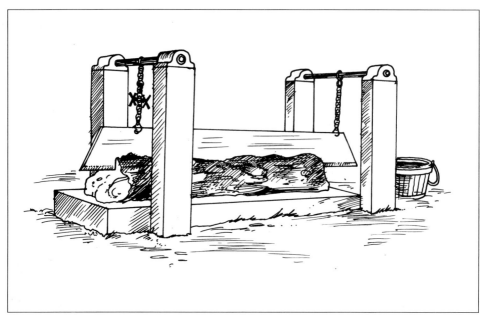

Artist's impression of a Swing Saw, approx. 12ft x 20 inches with 1/2 inch blade, of the type used at Blackingstone Quarry to cut the granite.

Water filled Blackingstone Quarry.

The Old Forge, Blackingstone.

*Waste stone and the Old Forge. A stone inscribed 1921 is visible
just below the apex of the Old Forge.*

The author in the old doorway of the forge at Blackingstone.

BRIDFORD EXCAVATIONS

As the river flows seawards through the steeply wooded valley, it is crossed twice within the next few miles; firstly by Clifford Bridge, of recent construction, and secondly by Steps Bridge, just outside Dunsford, which carries the B3212 Moretonhampstead to Exeter carriageway. Half a mile west of the bridge there is a disused quarry which has been cut into the steep slopes of Bridford Wood and has been extensively used, GR. 798-882. The opening on to the road measures about 50yds, the floor to the base of the cliff is about 60 feet and the face itself about 100 feet high. There is little waste at the top so that had not been a problem. There are no details of its use, but it seems to have been the site from which stone was taken for road repairs many years before the Local Authorities became responsible for our highways.

Across the road there is a panoramic view of the River Teign towards Clifford Bridge and the steep drop of 1 in 3 to the river 200 feet below.

On the far side of the river, Dunsford village, with its thatched houses and ancient church, lies against the hills which lead to Tedburn St. Mary. Records show that the most northerly situated mine, Wheal Anna Maria, was here, producing for a short period around 1846-47 the minerals quartz and iron pyrite, a little copper but no lead. Further south and on the west side of the river, Wheal Lawrence produced a small quantity of copper in about 1851. Unfortunately there are no physical features visible of either operation, except for spoil heaps located on the O.S. map GR. 813-884.

THE BRIDFORD BASALT AND GRANITE COMPANY QUARRY

Also known as Paddy Dixon's Quarry GR. 823-865, it lies on both the north and south side of Pound Lane, the road leading from the B3193 to the village of Bridford. There are three large areas of excavation; its vast size indicates that many thousands of tons of rock have been recovered since its opening in the late 19th century. The three worked faces vary in elevation between 500 and 650 feet above sea level. Rock from the higher pit was carried by tramway through to the next quarry, then by further narrow gauge track around the hill to the third working face. From here the tubs were lowered to the valley floor by means of the same narrow gauge incline tramway with a fall of 1 in 4.

With the arrival of the railway at the nearby Barytes Mine, the removal of the stone from this quarry became simpler. A public road crosses this steep incline and a small hump-backed bridge is still used to this day. At a glance it is easy to see the steepness of the hill where the track was laid.

Bridge over the incline. Paddy Dixons. Bridford.

Settling ponds. Bridford Barytes Mine.

With one exception the three quarries are overgrown with trees and vegetation, but old surveys show the existence of a large pond in the higher workings. It is easy to picture horse drawn vehicles approaching the tramway on the steep Bridford Hill and the clatter of steel on steel as the wheels came over the rails.

BRIDFORD BARYTES MINE 1875-1958. GR. 829-864

Although previous mining earlier in the 19th century had extracted small amounts of lead, it was the discovery of large quantities of barytes which led to the prosperity of this mine. The average width (6 feet) of the barytes veins, encouraged the mining company to expand its production. Barytes is a heavy, brownish mineral used as a base material for the manufacture of many important chemicals: barium carbonate, which is used in highly finished glass for television tubes, barium sulphate, which is an ingredient in the preparation of paint and as a filler for paper making, and other barium compounds which are used as additives in lubricating oils. It was also used during the war to make a fire retardant coating for the decks of battleships.

The mine was first known as Bridford Wheal Augusta, in 1849, and subsequently became Bridford Barytes in 1850. The workings were originally open cast and the mineral would have been taken away by horse and waggon along the track on the south side of the hill, passing a small quarry in the hillside and then across a field to join the valley road. The cart track is shown clearly on the 1905 Ordnance Survey as being on the north side of Rookery Brook. The survey is dated 1886 but has been updated to 1905.

With the arrival of the South Devon Railway in 1882, it became apparent that a railway could be laid up to the mine. This involved spanning the river, crossing the valley road and following the brook on to its south side, and with a gradient of 1 in 45, reaching the mine.

Later the mine was owned by the Malehurst Barytes Company and finally by Laporte Chemicals Ltd. Deep mining had now become the pattern. The wide veins encountered gave reasonable access to the mineral which has been followed to a depth of 500 feet (about 230 feet below sea level). The material was raised in skips which automatically tipped on reaching the surface. At every 100 feet tunnel roadways were driven into the mine following likely veins. Upon reaching the surface the material was taken by conveyor belt to be washed, thus separating the barytes from any impurities. The finished product was then ready for transportation, firstly by the mine railway until 1928 and subsequently by lorry to nearby Christow Station. There is record of a memo sent in 1931 by G.W.R. Head Office to the Station Master at Christow demanding an explanation as to why the bridge carrying the railway across the River Teign had not been demolished. It was presumably acted upon as no bridge survives today.

The miners, most of whom came from Bridford and Christow were under the supervision of a Mr. John Stuart, who unfortunately met with a fatal accident while carrying out a deep mine inspection on 15th September, 1954. The mine was closed in 1958.

Mrs E. Hocking, the wife of an engineer at the time, can remember being told by Mr. Surridge, one time of Bridford Mill, that the barytes used to be brought by horse and cart to the Mill to be ground. The result was something very like flour. Apparently the area around the mine was in danger of subsidence, as he had told Mrs Hocking that one morning the road between the cottage adjoining the lane and Bridford Hill fell in and that Mr. Gove, who lived there, didn't know whether his daughter had fallen down the hole.

The numerous settling ponds are now all that bear witness to a once thriving industry which must surely have had such an impact upon the local economy and also upon the character of the landscape, judging from the details of many building works that were carried out for the mining companies set down in Samuel Clark's account books.

BIRCH ELLERS MINE, 'MANY WATERS' BRIDFORD. GR. 826-871

Records show considerable activity in 1853 when the agent, Captain George Odgers of Camborne came to the mine. A shaft to the depth of 50 fathoms exposed lead and silver. The company was able to sell 25 tons of lead and 126 ounces of silver up to 1855. However, due to failure in finding profitable lodes, the mine closed. The 30 inch cylinder, 8ft stroke steam engine and the 30ft diameter water wheel together with the large boiler were sold. The Mining Journal suggested the mine was badly sited.

There still stands the granite built vent shaft on the west side of the path and the base of the engine-horse. This structure measured 18ft x 22ft externally with walls 4ft in thickness. The opening positioned on the south face suggests that the shaft must also have been on the south of the engine-house.

In the lower copse there is a large pit near the water-course, obviously big enough to have been the wheel-pit for the 30ft diameter water wheel. There are numerous spoil heaps in the area. Upon closure of the mine all the plant and machinery was put up for auction and an extract from the Exeter Flying Post 1.6.1855 read as follows.

Mr. John Ware is instructed to offer for sale, by Public Auction, on the Mine, on

Wednesday, the 13th day of June next, at one o'clock in the afternoon, all that valuable SETT, known as the Birch Aller Mine, situate in the parish of Bridford, in the county of Devon, together with the whole of the machinery, plant and all other materials, in and upon the same. The whole will first be offered in ONE LOT, and if not sold, then in separate lots, as described in catalogues, which will be ready for delivery one week prior to the sale.

The machinery consists of a 30-inch cylinder pumping engine, 8 feet stroke, with 8-ton boiler, etc., complete; capstan and shears; capstan rope; about 50 fathoms of 9 inch and 12 inch pumps and all necessary connections; 100 fathoms of 2 inch by half inch iron rail; horse whim, and 60 fathoms of 6-inch rope; a 30 feet water wheel; drawing machine; rods, chains, kibbles, ladders, launders; carpenters', smiths' and miners' tools; counting-house fittings, old and new timber etc., etc.

The above mine is situate about one mile north of Wheal Exmouth, and on the same very productive lode.

For particulars, apply to the Agent on the Mine; or to Mr. George Pye, Gandy Street; or at the Office of the Auctioneer, Paris Street, Exeter. Dated Paris Street, May 29th, 1855.

Artist's impression of an Engine House.

Remains of Birch Ellers Mine.

DODDISCOMBSLEIGH

Over the river at Doddiscombsleigh, there can be found the workings known as Harehill Plantation Mine, some 450 yards south of the church, GR. 858-863. They appear to be little more than an exploration consisting of a shallow shaft, an adit and overgrown openwork. The spoil heaps consist of hard, black rocks and coloured wastes believed to have been left in about 1878.

A small quarry lies about 100 yards due south of Woodah Farm. Similar to many small excavations and known locally as the 'old quarry', the extracted material may have been used for filling rough tracks or as building stone. By scale rule the face appears to be approximately 40 feet in width. There are a number of buildings in the parish with stone closely resembling jasper in texture and colour which may have originated from the site.

More workings can be found at Scanniclift Mine, south-east of Christow Station, now almost completely hidden by trees and vegetation. There are many inlets, one of which is large enough to enter without bending forward. It is now many years since the author visited the site and walked along the level tramways. According to his grandfather his forebears had once worked these seams. To the north-east, at the top of the field opposite Lake Farm, there are waste tips, possibly material taken out of an adit which has since collapsed. They are however more likely to be the outcroppings of the defunct Teign Mine as recorded in 1936.

Manganese, if pure, can be used in the manufacture of very hard steel and to alloy with copper, brass and nickel. If alloyed with iron as ferro manganese it can be used in the making of mild steel.

The ore would have been taken from the mines in this area to Exeter by pack-horse. In Doddiscombsleigh, approximately 400 yards north of the village road which links the school to the B3193, and at a point near Lake House, once known as Meyrtle Cottage, is the old track linking the pack-horse trail from the mine workings to what was Lake Cottage on the 1886 survey. To arrive at the property meant crossing an ancient stone-built bridge over Batts Brook, GR. 850-870. Although almost half has collapsed it is still wide enough for one person to cross. The author recognised local stones used in its construction and the lime and shale mortar mix; the stones of a light brown colour are common in this area. There is no parapet or any evidence of there having been one.

The owner of the property has kindly offered information on the old Lake Cottage. It was once occupied by one Stephen de Lake in 1249 and no doubt the old walls held stories of many a deed in this delightful valley. He also mentioned that it was possibly used as Mine Offices during the busy mining period when pack-horses would have been passing on their way to Exeter, laden down with the ore.

The cottage, 25ft x 25ft was set against a high bank with ground and first floor rooms, two up and two down. A recess niche gave access to the first floor with a very narrow wood-tread stair curving to the left. Cruck beams and cross rafters formed the roof of the thatch. Interestingly, all the windows were heavily barred against intruders. As in many instances the old cottage became unsafe and it collapsed about 1971 and a new bungalow was erected on the site.

ASHTON - MANGANESE MINING

During the early years of the 19th century and possibly even earlier, several tons of manganese were extracted in the Ashton area, making Devon the only county where it was to be found at this time. The 1905 O.S. map shows two areas of excavation some 500 yards west of Higher Barton Farm, north of the parish church. The excavated materials are in spoil heaps approximately 50 to 70 feet long by about 20 feet wide.

Further records from 1936 mention shallow excavations and a shaft 300 yards north-east of Higher Barton known as Wells Head Great Pit and a further line of workings known as Kiln Lode.

The author alongside the ancient stone bridge over Batts Brook.

HIGHER ASHTON QUARRY

An old map of 1886 clearly shows a quarry in the higher part of the parish of Ashton. It has been excavated and used for a similar purpose as many small quarries in the valley. As it is only about 500 yards west-north-west of the Old Rectory, no doubt the incumbent had some say in the repair of the road to Ashton Church. It has an approach track off George Teign Barton road; maybe the former owner of this listed property also benefited from the close proximity of stone ballast. Still in Ashton, but lying right on the east bank of the river, GR. 843-847, the Ryecroft Quarry was opened in 1930 and run as a family business. Sometimes known as 'Mill's Stone', the intention was to extract basalt from the wooded hill of Ryecroft. At the commencement of the operations, all materials were transported by road, but after serious consideration the G.W.R. provided a siding from the Teign Valley line into the quarry on the east side, together with a level crossing. Ownership then passed to Stoneycombe Basalts Ltd. Later a reinforced bridge crossed the river. The bridge exists today and appears to be in good repair. The author, on a later owner's instructions, engaged a diver, John Ridd, from Brixham to examine the footings after one of the worst recent flooding periods. He reported all to be sound in the river bed area.

Ryecroft did not yield a large quantity of good stone and that fact, coupled with the amount of waste, hastened the end of the business. The quarry closed down early in World War II and very little evidence remains of its existence.

SCATTER ROCK (SCATOR)
CHRISTOW COMMON. GR 820-856.

Before man had started to plunder this whole area for stone and minerals to meet his growing needs, Scator, between the villages of Bridford and Christow, the most easterly of the Dartmoor tors, although not granite, had risen to almost 1000 feet above sea level. There was a trigonometric station at its highest point in 1905. The tor was of blue-grey basalt and the massive, prominent crest had, at some time, been split asunder, the cleft being just wide enough for children to enter, and giving the impression of two gigantic shoulders hunched over the landscape. Today however, there is a disused quarry and a vast water-filled pit, the whole tor having been blown up shortly after the war to provide material for road building and the construction industry.

After the cessation of hostilities in 1945, the demand for stone inevitably increased and the floor of the original quarry was opened up and a huge pit some 300 yards in diameter was slowly excavated with a final depth of up to 80 feet.

The crushing plant had been installed at the base of the hill some 400 feet lower. An incline with double tracks enabled the descending trucks, each carrying approximately 1½ tons to hoist the empty ones up to the top, the speed of descent regulated by a large braking drum some 10 feet in diameter and 18 inches in width. To obviate undue wear on the 1 inch hawser, greased rollers were set in between the rails at 12 feet intervals. On arrival at the lower level the trucks were unhooked from the cable and a heavy horse then pulled them on level tracks around the side of the hill to the crushing machines, the contents of each truck then being tipped into the shute.

In warm, dry weather, dust rose in clouds as the machinery crushed the rocks. The crushed stones then passed through the screens of variable mesh, thence into the containers. It was from this point that transportation changed. An aerial ropeway conveyed the material overhead to Christow station, about one mile distant, where the ever moving buckets (3ft x 4ft) were tipped into concrete hoppers set over the rail trucks of the Teign Valley line, with a goods engine in attendance to move the loaded waggons which carried the name of 'Scatter Rock Macadam' on their sides. With the entry of America into the Second World War, a large military facility was needed at Lympstone requiring the construction of jetties and bank strengthening, and the small lower quarry near the crushing plant had come into full use. A large mechanical navvy loaded the six-wheel Chevrolet lorries with broken stone and for many weeks the 'Yanks', as the locals called them, ferried their loads along the narrow roads on the way to the B3193 and their destination.

The Scatter Rock Quarry ceased operations in 1950 and now the area has become overgrown. The pit has become a small lake, birch trees have sprouted everywhere and gorse and bracken cover large areas. Peace has returned and wild life is in abundance. It is not advisable to visit any part of the complex, firstly because it is on private land and secondly, the lake is very deep and in its depths are rusty metal objects, steel hawsers and other debris ready to trap the unsuspecting diver.

·SCATTER ROCK MACADAMS·
━━━━ LIMITED ━━━━
(SUBSIDIARY OF ROADS RECONSTRUCTION (1934) LTD.)

Telephone: FROME 430 (4 lines)
Telegrams: UPKEEP, Frome

STONELEIGH HOUSE,
FROME,
SOMERSET

............24th.April.........1945...

Received from   W.G.Clark Esq.,

the sum of

Nine--pounds

Seven----------shillings and   Six--------pence.

£ 9. 7. 6d.

With Compliments
SCATTER ROCK MACADAMS, Ltd.

FOR TEIGN VALLEY CONCRETE COMPNAY LIMITED

Secretary

W.G.Clark Esq.,
Builder,
CHRISTOW,
Nr. Exeter.

Copy of receipt for payment of materials purchased from Scatter Rock Macadams, 1945.

The water filled Scatter Rock Quarry.

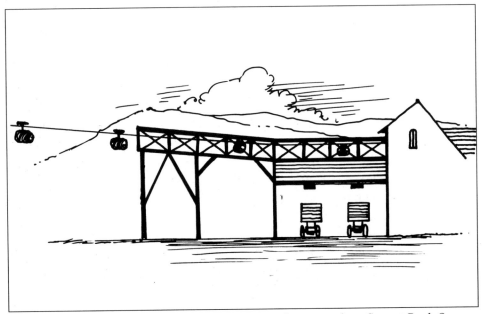

The terminal, Christow Station, for the aerial ropeway from Scatter Rock Quarry.

A very old photo taken in 1920 showing work on the Scatter Rock Quarry face.
A Mr J. Major watches workmen below.
Photo permission Mr J. Major.

The Legend of Old Scator

Old Scator had rested upon his 1,000 ft hill-top for many millions of years, his two massive shoulders formed in blue-grey rock. Each stood twenty-five feet high and lacking a head was of little consequence, it was his ageless spirit that mattered. The bedrock upon which he stood went down into the depths of the hill. At times he glanced to the north west, where granite formed Heltor Rock stood, or to the west where the rounded top of loaf shaped Blackingstone reared its head, but he was different from either, his body was harder and formed of basalt, he was also the most easterly of the Dartmoor tors.

Since his appearance all those years ago most changes had occurred within the last 8,000 years. There was the howl of the wolves, the bears, and the wild sabre-tooth cat. To the south, three large families of humans had occupied round stone-based grass covered huts. They hunted their prey with spear or bow and arrow, covering their bodies with skins.

Most prominent in his memory was the chill of the ice age when the land became covered with snow and ice, the frosts penetrated many feet into the soil and the river remained frozen year in, year out. Very few animals existed then, only the moaning of the cold north wind for company. Since that experience there has been great climatic changes, vegetation sprang up around him, trees grew in abundance and the wild life appeared again. Recently the human race increased in numbers, they built their homes of stone and cob with thatched roofs, setting them up in groups or settlements. One such collection lay a mile to the north, another a mile to the south east. It was from these settlements that old Scator had heard the wailing cries of the bereaved when the Black Death took its toll. At night he could hear the mournful toll of bells in the two churches, most persistent from the northern one.

By this time men and women living nearby had begun to cultivate large areas of land some as close to the Tor as 100 yards. Their constant comings and goings interested him, especially when their children tried to climb his sides or hide in the huge crevice where he had once been split open.

He also could recall the earthquake on 23rd December 1661, when his whole body shook with the great vibrations, animals panicked, birds flew off their roosts and although it lasted but half a minute he was much disturbed below ground level. By the 20th Century, Scator became aware of digging operations taking place upon his eastern slopes, quarrymen arrived and began cutting into his side; the rock proved hard to extract, and much blasting occurred. Day in, day out, they worked, the stone being loaded into tubs for the long journey down the incline where the crushing plant broke every piece within its huge jaws.

Bridford Barytes Mine, about 1950.
Photo reproduced permission of Maurice Stuart.

BRIDFORD BARYTES MINE, about 1950.

The workforce line up for a photo-session.

Among those standing rear

Harry Burchell, Charlie Hamlyn, Ron Sharp, Walt Gove, Fred Waldon, Charlie Hodge, Bert Symns, John Backhouse, George Collins, Edgar Gove, Jack Major, Cliff Cox, Harry Ebdon, Jim Bray, George Cutland, Hector Elliott, Bert Collins, Bill Bushin.

Among those standing below

Bill Morgan, Rueben Elliott, Albert Noon, Frank Lewis, Les Miller, George Counter, Ron Lawes, Jack Payne, Bill Jones, John Stuart (Manager), Jim Pearson, Vic Mann, Sam George, Harry Bickleigh, Eric Gove, Reg Gosling, Bert Waldron, Jim Mitchell, Unknown, Alf Keys, Alf Stonelake, Les Pearson, Fred Ware, Cecil Gove, Bill Grey, Jack Waldron, Bert Miller, Same Collins.

Checking the water outfall - Bridford Barytes Mine. L to R. Bill Morgan, John Stuart (Manager) ... Lancaster, about 1950. Photo reproduced permission of Maurice Stuart.

As the years went by the quarry face came nearer to his position, the blasting causing a shaking sensation every time a charge exploded. Meanwhile, at the base of the hill, further inroads had been made to extract stone for use as a loading platform. Humans from far away America came in their hugh six-wheel trucks to carry it away.

It was at this time that Old Scator encountered a much different experience. Away to the south west on most nights, brilliant flashes lit the sky. On occasions when the south west wind blew he could hear loud detonations and then on the night air a thin wailing noise as if it were an animal in agony. One night, having witnessed the display, he heard the roar of something in the sky and in the light of a full moon two flying things came out of the west. He saw their outlines, one had large wings, the other much smaller. Suddenly flashes came from both, there was a rat-tat-tat again and again, flames spouted from the larger of the birds and then came a loud explosion near the base of the hill followed by more rat-tat-tat. As the two moved out of sight, Scator rested again.

Within a few months poor Scator knew his end was near, a hole beneath his body was packed with short, round, candle-like pieces. a long string attached was lit; it seemed to go out, but the sizzling string came to life, its hissing coming nearer every second, men ran for cover, the sizzling end disappeared into the hole. There was an eerie silence, then, with a deafening roar the charge exploded. Scator's base stones lifted him high, first one shoulder then the other fell and together they plunged 100 feet to the quarry floor to be further broken and spread throughout the area as builders' sand or for road repairs. So ended the presence of the most easterly of the Dartmoor tors. Old Scator was destroyed, but his ghost still haunts the far shore.

The following extract appeared in the Express and Echo newspaper during the summer of 1920.

DEVON MINERALS
BIG DEVELOPMENT IN TEIGN VALLEY
ROADSTONE & IRON ORE

About 80 members of the Exeter Chamber of Commerce spent a most interesting half-day on Tuesday visiting the Scatter Rock Quarries at Christow, where a large roadstone industry is being developed. The majority of the visitors were surprised at the extent of the developments already made, and these will be dwarfed by the extensions in contemplation.

It was appropriate, therefore, that the Chamber of Commerce should be afforded an opportunity of seeing what is being done, and, through the kindness of Mr Arthur C. Thomas (Chairman of the Chamber) and Mr John Dickson (Managing Director) and the directors of the Scatter Rock Macadam Co., an instructive business trip was happily combined with pleasure. The party, which included Sir Robert Newman M.P. (president of the Chamber), were driven in motor charabancs to Christow, where they first inspected the terminal plant by means of which the stone (brought from the rock face two miles away by aerial cable-ways) is crushed to size for road-making, or "granulated" for other purposes, and loaded with the aid of many ingenious devices into the railway trucks. Thence the party went to the quarry, where a pyrotechnic display of blasting was given for their diversion. The customary precautions were invested with interest to the uninitiated: the awesome sound of the hooter denoting that blasting was about to take place, the scattering of the swarm of men who at one moment appeared to inhabit the quarry face like industrious ants, and a few minutes afterwards were grouped in safety a hundred yards away, leaving half a dozen only to fire the fuses for charges already laid. Then, looking like fireflies, as watched from a vantage-point on the opposite side of a ravine, the darting flames of torches or tapers could be seen flitting here and there in the quarry. Here were men who run at their work! Presumably with the connivance of their unions, too. An interval, in which the steady roar of the warning siren alone broke the silence and then one after another a flash and a louder roar as the charges exploded, to be followed by the tearing sound of riven rock, an eruption of earth and stone, and a miniature avalanche of rock down the face of the quarry. A thousand tons of rock had been displaced, and with the silencing of the hooter the men returned to renew their task of removing stone for the unending task of renewing the face of the nation's highways.

ON THE SUMMIT OF SCATTER ROCK

Next the party faced the stiff climb up the newly-laid trolley-way to the top of the tor (Scatter Rock is thought to be a corruption of Skat Tor). The trolley-way is awaiting trolleys ordered 14 months ago, and still undelivered, in consequence of the moulders' strike and other delays. At the top of the climb Mr Thomas's otherwise perfect ciceroneship failed. He had promised a glimpse of the Channel, but the mists were in between. Nevertheless, the party obtained a glorious panorama under a westering sun, and they were also able to get an idea of the big developments contemplated on the western side of the tor. It is possible to foresee the sacrifice of the rugged head of the tor and the rich mineral lode beneath to the exigencies of the modern holiday of charabanc and motor 'bus'. At present the output of Scatter Rock stone, which has been demonstrated by expert tests to be the hardest in England, is 1,250 tons a week. Its possibilities are practically limited only by labour and transport resources and the demand is much greater than can at present be supplied. The party returned to Exeter via Chudleigh and Haldon. Tea was provided at the quarry by the company, and Sir Robert Newman, M.P., proposed a vote of thanks to Mr Dickson and the hosts, saying the Chamber was keenly interested in everything which affected the commercial welfare of the city, and owed a debt of gratitude to the energy and fore-sight with which the industry was being developed. Mr Arthur Thomas acknowledging thanks for his share of the day's proceedings, said there were big developments in the heart of the Teign Valley in concequence of the demand for hard roadstone to cope with the heavy traffic.

Just a few hundred yards south-east of Scatter Rock Quarry are three bronze age stone circles and evidence of a field system, GR 824-854. A mile to the south west lies Clampitt Farm. In the 17th Century, a Quaker family settled at this isolated site to join their friends. Peaceful though they were, the authorities outlawed them and they were persecuted by some local people. Vicious attacks occurred at their meeting but failed to dissuade them from continuing. Later, a small plot near the farm became their burial ground. A lime kiln exists about 300 yards north-west of Clampitt House. Just west of Clampitt lies Kennick Reservior. The construction of the dam across the reservoir and all its ancillary works was supervised by Henry Brunel, son of the famous Isambard Kingdom Brunel. At the western end of the dam there is an open area with the fishing permit building sitting neatly upon it. The space once held a large amount of solid stone and when the earth dam was completed and all the clay from Christow claypitts laid, the face looking north had to be cased with stone as a protection against water-wave erosion; hence the small quarry, being close, was used to provide the necessary material.

CHRISTOW -BROOKS QUARRY
GR. 841-846

This now disused quarry lies roughly four hundred yards south of Ashton Mill Weir, on the west side of the B3193. Its brown stone does not appear to be as durable as other samples in the valley, a thick 'overburden' of loose shale and earth obviously contributed to its inevitable closure. However, in its heyday during the late 19th century, the quarry's owner, a Mr Brooks, supplied material for keeping the valley road in reasonable repair for horse drawn vehicles. The width of the access is approximately 29 yds wide, the depth to the base 33 yds and the quarry face approximately 100 ft high.

The following extract is taken from the minutes of Christow Parish Council the date of the resolution being November, 18th, 1895 and refers to 'stones required to repair the valley road between Ashton Bridge and the Teign House Inn.' There is no mention of the final surface appearance, so one can assume a rough, pitted and rutted track running between Ashton Bridge and the Teign House Inn.

At a meeting of the Christow Parish Council held in the Schoolroom after due notice on Monday, November 18th, present, the chairman and full council. The minutes of the last meeting were read and confirmed. It was unanimously resolved that the following resolution would be sent to Mr Arthur Ward to lay before the District Council.

"The Parish Council of Christow respectfully beg to request the District Council to allow the stones required for the repair of their roads (especially the lower road leading from Ashton Bridge to Teign House) to be drawn from the quarry that Mr Brooks is at present working in the lower road, as they consider it would save expense in drawing and spreading, and also they express their surprise that that stone which has been so extensively used by the Town Council of Exeter, and approved by competent judges should be rejected by the surveyor of the highways without, as it appears to them, sufficient reason".

Signed C.J. Bulteel

BENNAH MINE - CHRISTOW GR. 834-847

While in conversation with Mr. Nick Tuckett, whose family have resided here for many generations, several items of information came to light.

The mine is situated some 100yds south west of a property known as Bennah Villa. A shaft, now collapsed and almost full, is thought to be the grave of a pony who, many years ago, fell to its death many fathoms below. There are spoil heaps visible nearby and the remains of the engine house base are still to be seen in the neighbouring property. The dimensions of the latter as far as he can recall are about 20ft by 30ft. His father, William Tuckett, left him further details before he died, namely, on the north end of the house are outbuildings which were drying sheds for the mine. The ground floor rooms at the rear served as the Mine Offices. Manganese was bought to the surface together with 'shiney-ore', and sent by horse and wagon to Exeter, presumably to the ship canal.

Further conversation revealed that the levels from the shaft ran towards Hill Farm to the south and this may account for the waste heaps which lie west-north-west and are shown as simple marks on the 1886 survey map.

ALLER MINE - CHRISTOW

The listed farmhouse known as Aller is situated on a south facing slope of a small valley. Due south, and within 500yds on the other side of the valley stream, is a large ivy covered building, GR. 836-839. There is so much of the clinging growth that at first it appears to be an extremely wide tree trunk, however the stone-built structure is a disued engine house known locally as Wheal Adam or Addems, a family closely connected with the area and at one time the owners of Reed and Aller Farm. Local registers give the name of Nathaniel Addems.

The main walls are in a poor state of repair and if the ivy were removed most of the structure would no doubt collapse. Nearby are adits and spoil heaps which, if examined, would possibly show evidence of lead, zinc and manganese. The entrance is off Reed Lane, a cul-de-sac in the area of Coombe Cross. 100yds north-west is an adit in the north bank of the stream, emitting a constant flow of water.

REED MINE - CHRISTOW GR. 836-837

Just 200yds south of Reed Farm House and on rising ground is the site of a mine building, now partly demolished, commonly known by local people as Reed Mine. A standing wall appears to be the position of an engine house. The nearby waste heaps indicate that there had been considerable activity during the 19th century, with lead and zinc being much sought after. Geologists were well aware of the underground treasure, silver being of significant quantity to warrant the extensive mining undertaken in that period.

The nearby cottages no doubt housed some of the miners and their families as did many of the small cottages in the Valley, one group comprising three dwellings and known as Byteign or Bittin and another as Hill Park Cottages. These were converted by the author into single residences in 1960 and 1963 respectively.

THE SHUTTAMOOR MINE (IRON)

The area known locally as 'Shootimoor' is in a valley west of the Canonteign Estate, running west to east not far from Shuttamoor Farm. The site is now covered by dense vegetation and marsh and is a retreat for wildlife, almost inaccessible and, of course, on private land. The stream is the possible source of the Canonteign Falls.

The iron lode beneath runs eastward to link with other lodes at Frank Mills and Hennock Mine. Operations commenced about 1890 and finished early this century. During that period there were difficulties in finding ore of an acceptable quality, this bringing the mining to an end.

An old survey of 1905, shows a long building near a leat and two others, a tip for waste, a shaft and two air vents and a track leading west to the Christow - Bovey Tracey road.

WHEAL EXMOUTH MINE (LEAD AND SILVER) - CHRISTOW

The site is approximately 500yds south of the granite-built Elizabethan Manor House at Canonteign, once in the ownership of Viscountess Exmouth, but now privately owned. The mining complex is on the east side of the unclassified road from Christow Village to Chudleigh, GR. 838-830.

It comprises a tall boiler chimney shaft which has a very ornate top of small arches supported on protruding stone corbels; the main stack is built in random stone. Adjoining are the partly demolished walls of a building. The engine house is within a few feet of the road and stands in a commanding position. Its height of four storeys, plus a span-slated roof reaches above the trees. The new owner has restored the building tastefully and it has now returned to its former glory, plus having provided a very comfortable home. Nearby there is another chimney shaft for what was possibly a large boiler house. This structure is octagonal and measures approximately 10 feet across the flats. Each angle is formed in cut granite in alternate courses. A close inspection of the granite structure indicates its similarity to the stone at Blackingstone Quarry, mentioned earlier. Unfortunately the upper portion has collapsed and complete restoration would necessitate the shaping of more granite angles for each of the eight sides, plus the erection of scaffolding to at least 40 feet.

A stone wall backing onto the road was the rear of store sheds for the mine and within 100 yds are the buildings which were once the blacksmith's shop, mine offices and miners' cottages. Eastwards down the valley, are the waste dumps. These reach as far as the valley road and the River Teign.

A considerable workforce operated the mine in the 19th century, the engine house being the largest in the valley with its massive rocking beam and huge boiler. However, the lead lodes were eventually worked out and by 1875 the

Chimney shaft showing arches and stone corbels.

mine was closed. During its life-time the mine raised 11,570 tons of 65% lead ore and 118,000 ounces of silver (1851-1875) and 1,560 tons of zinc ore produced in the same period.

In August 1977, a planning application was submitted to the local authority (Dartmoor National Park) by a company who intended processing the waste dumps of the mine; their intention being to refine the material and retain any metals during the operation. The waste would then be taken to the old Whetcombe Quarry pit and dumped.

There were many objections to the proposal from different bodies of varied interests, the Teign fishermen, environmentalists, The Wild Life Trust, anti-pollution experts, traffic control, etc., and even those who considered the mounds should remain untouched.

After a site inspection by Dartmoor National Park, Devon County Council, Teignbridge District Council, The Highways Department, Christow Parish Council and the Company named in the application, it was not approved and in consequence the view from the valley road remains unaltered.

Wheal Exmouth. Octagonal chimney and restored engine house, now a private dwelling.

Wheal Exmouth engine house before restoration.

Wheal Exmouth waste tips.

* Wheal is a Cornish word for 'Huel' meaning a hole.

HENNOCK - FRANK MILLS MINE GR. 836-820

The workings are in an area known as Hyner. They are about 500yds west of Hyner Farm, almost at the end of a cul-de-sac track. A partly demolished engine house and stack together with a few stone-built shed walls and vast spoil dumps are all that remain of this once prosperous enterprise.

Although the mine is approximately half a mile south from Wheal Exmouth, it is known that they were connected, due to two factors; one, that the ore lodes in the Teign Valley were running north to south and secondly that at one period the two were under joint management. The engine shaft passes between the east and west lodes and has been sunk to a great depth (over 100 fathoms).

Frank Mills Engine House.

Notes detailed by Provis. (Geological researcher) 1874.
This mine produced 70.5% metallic lead with 25 ozs of silver per ton, and later 60.5% lead and 25.25 ozs of silver per ton.
The final recorded outputs are:-

| 1856-80 | 14,800 tons of 67% lead ore, 248,500 ozs of silver, 240 tons haematite, 1880 tons spathic iron ore, some fluorspar and 870 tons of barytes. |

On the south wall in Christow Church is a tablet reading
Fixed in memory of Joseph Nicholls.
Mine agent at Frank Mills who died in 1869.

GREAT ROCK MINE. HENNOCK GR. 827-816

The valley in which the micaceous haematite (Shiney-ore) is found is near the boundary of the parish of Christow to the north and but a few hundred yards from Frank Mills. The lodes of almost pure metal run west to east out of the granite mass of Dartmoor and had an average width of 2 feet. A company by the name of Hennock Iron, Steel & Tin Mining operated at the site from 1849 to 1890 when, for undisclosed reasons it closed down.

Twelve years after the closure, a new firm, The Ferrubron Manufacturing Company, a German group, re-opened it. The mine captain was Will Hoskins and under his direction, adits were driven into the hill with railed tramways and these were the principle means of bringing the materials to the finishing sheds. The ore appeared clay-like before refining and after passing through a mill, water was used to wash out the silt, the ore then ran on into settling tanks from where it was dried to a powder and packed into barrels.

The First World War interrupted mining again and it was not until 1916 when the metal was much in demand, that a Mr. Slatter took over the site. There are details in Samuel Clark's account books which refer to the setting up of buildings at Great Rock, Hennock for a Mr. Slatter. By 1930 compressed air had been introduced for drilling purposes, but it was not until 1950 that electricity took the place of water power. The work force, whose number had once risen to 30 men were all made redundant when the mine finally closed in 1969. Mr. Arthur Ball of Christow worked there for 17 years as mine electrician and he has kindly supplied many items of information.

QUARRY

There is a further small quarry on the western side of the minor road linking the village of Chudleigh Knighton, GR 833-797. Because of its size and location, this site could have been in use for a similar purpose as that of the small quarry of Mr. Brooks at Christow, where the local council asked the owner to supply and lay hardcore in the ruts caused by carts and waggons before our roads were maintained by the County Highways Department.

RILEY MINE

This mine is in the vicinity of Riley Farm, to the west of Crockham Quarry and within an area east of Huish Cross. During its lifetime searches were made for manganese ore and several tons were sold. The site has been completely obscured since its closure about 1880. There were three groups of shafts and adits as stated in the 1904 and 1912 records. (Memoirs of Geological Survey of Great Britain) H.M.S.O. 1956.

SOUTH EXMOUTH MINE GR. 837-808

Also called by the locals Hennock Mine, sited south-east of Hennock Church and west-south-west of Teign Village, this is one of the most southerly of the Teign Valley mining ventures, but on the same lodes.

The operations began as early as 1850 and finished before 1870. An engine shaft was sunk to the 90 fathom level. Except for the spoil dumps very little remains. There is a record of 750 tons of 70% lead ore and 1,100 ozs of silver from details dated 1904 and 1912.

From Wheal Anna Maria at Dunsford to the South Exmoor Mine at Hennock is a distance of about four miles and yet we have seen that for a comparatively short period in the 19th century it was an area of intensive and large scale mining. There must have been at least eight engine houses with their nodding beams and smoking chimneys operating at the same time. The use of coal for the boilers involved the almost continuous stream of horse-drawn waggons bringing the fuel from the canal quay at Kingsteignton to the mines. Cornish miners and their families had come to the area, and the influx swelled the population to almost double its former number. They brought not only their expertise but also their Wesleyan or Methodist religion from Cornwall.

Methodist records show that during the mid-19th century there were meeting places at Ashton, Neadon and Leigh Cross Farm, close to the old mines of Birch Ellers and Wheal Anna Maria. It would seem that the mining community in the valley was the driving force behind the building of the new chapel, built at Christow in 1860-61. The chapel, stone built, possibly using mined materials has survived the years, its granite quoins and arches cut and fitted with loving care. Although it was closed in the 80s, the memories still live on for many in the local community as is the case re the disused chapel at Hennock; the Christmas Tree gathering for the children in December, the Good Friday teas and sports, the summer outings to the seaside in open charabancs and the Harvest Festival.

Religious rivalry existed in the valley for many generations. The existence of 'Church versus Chapel' is shown in the Parish Records and the author experienced this attitude during his early life. Today however, there is new blood in the valley and a vibrant community exists, with a fall in the average age of the population.

TRUSHAM - WHETCOMBE AND TINKLEY QUARRIES
GR. 844-819 - GR.846-816

Owned by the Teign Valley Granite Company, these pits are now filled with water infiltrating from the nearby river. They were bustling sites for stone extraction in their heyday. Old photographs show tram lines on the quarry floor converging to a point where the stone was lifted to ground level ready for removal. The two quarries are on the east bank of the river and approached from the entrance to Whetcombe Farm. Tinkley is on the south side and Whetcombe lies on the Ashton side. The quarries were in production until 1931 when the parent company took the decision to close them down.

OLD TRUSHAM QUARRY
GR. 850-813

Later known as 'Paddy Dixons', this quarry is on the east side of the River Teign and within a few hundred yards of the Old Trusham Station. About the turn of the century, the owner took advantage of the close proximity of the railway and soon had its own siding and ease of loading. There is a quarry face of about 80ft., with upper and lower floors and a deep water-filled pit. The Teign Valley Granite Co., eventually became the owners. It was used as a dump for waste materials and the site is well fenced and entry is forbidden.

Existing Quarry faces of (above) Old Trusham and (next page top) Whetcombe.

CROCKHAM QUARRY

This is now the only working quarry in the Teign Valley. There is a constant movement of lorries to and fro the weigh-bridge. Geologists' reports suggest there are over 6,000,000 tons of good stone lying beneath the surface. It is a tough, igneous rock, yet workable material of the basalt family, namely Dolerite, 2mm grain size, and until the closure of the adjoining concrete works it was also the basic aggregate for the huge pipes used by many Civil Engineers and County Councils.

The quarry opened around 1900, with the Teign Valley railway playing a major part in the expansion. Sidings were run into the crushing areas and trucks were quickly loaded with sand, graded chippings etc. By the end of that same year the daily tonnage sent by rail came to 500 tons. A labour intensive quarry absorbed the skills of 130 men from the surrounding countryside. The Manager, a Mr. R. Bathurst, organised gangs for the upper face (120ft) and lower face (60ft) quarries. The rock was then drilled by hand or stem-operated drill. The explosives for blasting were ammonal or dynamite, the stone breakers operated by steam. Revolving screens separated the various sizes of aggregate which were then fed down shutes into the rail trucks below, a separate gantry being used to feed large stones into the trucks. A shunting engine coupled to the trucks moved them forward across the main valley road(B3193), through the various sidings and on to the main line. As time went on traffic increased until an average of four loaded trains were dispatched daily. The Company owned many of the rail trucks and their name appeared on most.

The Teign Valley Granite Company also produced Targranix for the final coating of roads. This material was sent to many destinations, even as far as the southern counties.

Today, heavy lorries carry the materials to their destinations and then return for further loads. Unfortunately the concrete works are now closed, a sad end to a once thriving business.

The nearby hamlet known as Teign Village comprises over 50 houses and can be described as a street in a large field. The properties were erected in the early 20th century to accommodate the quarry employees and their families. The company maintained the houses for the following 50 years, and there are details in the books of the author's forebears showing works carried out both to the houses and at the quarry,

(above & below) Crockham Quarry.

plus receipts for sand, aggregate and stone purchased for other contracts in the Valley. During alterations to a property at Christow, demolition works uncovered hollow concrete blocks, 9 x 9 x 18 inches with the following imprint on their sides "Hennock Concrete Works".

CHUDLEIGH - LIMESTONE QUARRIES AND KILNS

The vast spectacle of Chudleigh Rocks GR. 864-787 is clearly visible on the south side of the old A38 if approaching from the west. Limestone must have been taken from this place since its use first became apparent. The caves beneath were inhabited by man and beast for thousands of years.

The large number of quarries in the parish are an indication of the value of limestone for the surrounding district, hence the number of kilns for burning the stone, and its use in building work. After the disastrous fire in the ancient wool town in 1807 houses had to be built for the homeless population and this may also account for the many quarrying sites.

To the north of the Parish and in close vicinity to the Whiteway Estate entrance is the now disused limestone quarry at Oxencombe. The amount of stone taken over a long period amounted to many thousands of tons. It was grey/pink in colour and formed an outcrop of East Ogwell limestone (see British Geological Survey).

At present, all that is visible is a green field, Devon County Council permitted the quarry to become a landfill site and after filling grass now adorns the hillside and the once torn field has returned to its former use.

Mr. E. Lee, a long-time resident of Chudleigh also mentioned the vast amount of stone taken from the district towards the building of the new bypass.

Grealy Quarry (Limestone), which is situated approximately half a mile east of the town cemetery, was the subject of approval in a planning application dated 4th August, 1959. Certain conditions were imposed for the future use as a quarry. It is not now in operation, but as in the case of other quarries a large amount of stone was used for the bypass construction. The face-workings are very close to a public highway leading to Haldon. Old lime kilns are shown on maps of the area.

Palace Quarry, east of Chudleigh Rocks, has been in operation for a long period and has given the area many thousands of tons of limestone.

The site has been the subject of planning applications on numerous occasions. In January, 1948, approval was granted for an extension to mineral workings for the Clifford Estate and April, 1960, saw the grant of approval for an office extension and rest room. In February, 1965, further permission was granted to extend the working area, but subject to five conditions, one being the problem of dust control. Kingston Minerals Ltd., applied for a further extension of quarrying in March, 1975 but this application was refused. It later went to appeal but was withdrawn in 1975.

CHUDLEIGH DISTRICT

Location of Quarries and Kilns with Grid References
(Approximate distances only are given)

400 yards West-north-west of Biddlestone School
         GR. 877-789   Old Quarry.

$^1/4$ mile West of Ugbrooke House, Quarry and lime kiln
         GR. 872-780

$^1/4$ mile East of Rock House Palace Quarry (Extensive) with two
lime kilns.   GR. 867-787

400 yards South-west of Mistleltoe Farm   Quarry and kiln
         GR. 889-805

500 yards North-west of Mistletoe Farm   Quarry
         GR. 889-802

$^1/4$ mile East of Amberley Farm at 'Ridge'   Quarry and kiln
         GR. 889-801

200 yards South-south-east of 'Ridge'   Quarry
         GR. 890-800

200 yards North-north-east of Amberley Farm with one kiln
         GR. 886-803

300 yards North-east of Lower Upcott   Extensive quarry
         GR. 886-804   and 2 kilns

300 yards North-north-west of Kerswell House   Quarry and kilns
         GR. 884-807

600 yards South-south-west of Lower Harcombe   Quarry
         GR. 884-812

Between and adjoining the A38 carriageways
         GR. 883-819   Extensive Quarry
         and kiln

700 yards South-west of Lower Harcombe (Holmans Wood)
         GR. 883-812   Quarry and kiln

Grealy Quarry Chudleigh, as it is today, a haven for wildlife.

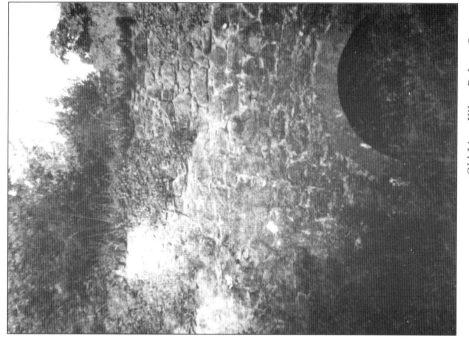

Old Lime Kiln - Palace Quarry.

Palace Quarry face, Chudleigh.

EMPLOYMENT

Mining operations had come to an end by about 1880, except for the barytes mine at Bridford and the micaceous haematite mine at Great Rock, due to the exhaustion of mineral lodes and increased overheads. Fortunately, unemployment in the area was alleviated by the opening of the large quarries, supplying the demand for stone, initially for new railway track, and by the turn of the century, for the nation's roads.

By the end of World War I and soon after, manual workers accounted for over 90% of the local male population. The railway had been extended up the valley and thence to Exeter with, at minimum, 8 trains a day plus goods trains.

Cottages were provided for the workers and their families, and many of these survive today, often adding to the character of the valley villages. Each small cottage had its own vegetable garden, and after 1894 the Parish Councils were duty bound to provide allotments if more than five families requested them. A number of quarry men and miners cultivated some of the wide road verges to grow potatoes and farm labourers were sometimes permitted to grow up to three rows of potatoes in their employers' fields. They were also granted the firewood and wood faggots from the newly layered hedges on the farm, thus cutting the cost of coal. Weekly markets were common and occurred within a reasonable distance of the communities, and here the housewife could replenish most of her requirements.

Most cottages and houses were equipped with furnaces, brick built and roughly 40 inches square. They were sometimes to be found in the rear kitchen or lean-to, but normally in the wood shed, thus being their only means of heating water for wash day or baths. It was common practice for the boiler to be lit for Friday evenings when the large metal bath would be in use for the whole family. Candles were superseded by paraffin until main electricity arrived. Gas was available in the valley towns.

The wealth of metal, mineral and building stone beneath the ground has always been seized at the cost of human life and there were no doubt numerous casualties and indeed fatalities that occurred in the Teign Valley operations. Mention has already been made of Mr John Stuart's death at the Bridford Barytes Mine in 1954. Going back in the industry's past, Mr. Hamlyn-Parsons, a past Head Teacher in the Valley states that in the 16th century a man 'died at his worke' at Canonteign. He contends that the word 'worke' at that time referred to mining operations.

The presence of carbon dioxide in the workings on occasions had to be overcome by building a platform almost as far as the face of the lode. This long erection created an air-flow. The incoming air ran over the top and was expelled along the space beneath.

The other gas, carbon monoxide, had a similar effect in that it also put the candle flame out, but beforehand the flame changed colour, thus giving adequate warning. The miners had to take action and retire at once otherwise they would become sleepy with shaking limbs and fatal results. The gas was also known as cold damp. Today Radon Gas is frequently found in old workings and warnings have been given by the local authorities in the area bordering the National Park.

THE BOVEY BASIN

From Chudleigh the Teign takes a more leisurely course and makes its way to join the rivers Bovey and Lemon near Newton Abbot. At a point just south of Chudleigh Knighton, white clay can be seen clearly on the river bed. This is the edge of the ball-clay bearing land known as the Bovey Basin. The author can recall the aroma of the burning lignite or 'brown coal' excavated from the clay works wafting up the valley on the strong south-westerly winds before such burning ceased.

Newton Abbot is on the main railway line from Paddington to Penzance, but it is also an important junction for Torquay and formerly to the Teign Valley and Mortonhampstead lines. The huge goods yards have dealt with ballast, aggregate, rock, clay and other commodities, employing many men from the town.

Moving further down the River Teign, a disused quarry GR. 884-740 is shown between Kingsteignton and Bishopsteignton, lying on the north side of the valley. Just south-west of this grid reference lies another quarry, now known as the Bickley Ball refuse tip. From here the river is tidal and with the constant ebb and flow of the water and the ever settling of silt brought into the valley from the moors and the smaller tributaries, it became necessary to constantly dredge the channels in order to keep them open for boat traffic.

The following text has been compiled from information provided by Watts Blake and Bearne & Co. PLC. Newton Abbot.

DEVON BALL CLAYS

The term 'ball clay' is applied to plastic sedimentary clays, high in kaolinite, which posses white firing properties and high green strength. The name 'ball clay' derives not from any specific property of the clay but from the original method of production, which consisted of cutting out the clay in open pits into cubes 22 to 25cm each weighing 14 to 16kg.

The ball clays of Devon have been in general use in pottery compositions in the British Isles since the latter half of the 17th century, and since the middle of the 19th century they have been exported to countries throughout Europe and to the United States. They are now marketed extensively throughout the world and owe their continuing popularity to their unique and consistent combination of physical properties.

The clays are won from two separate deposits. One, located near Bovey Tracey, is known as 'The Bovey Basin'; the other, located near Peters Marland, about 1.5 kilometres to the east of the village of Petrockstow in North Devon.

The important Sticklepath-Lustleigh Fault system extends from Torquay to North Devon and on into the Bristol Channel. This fault system played a major part in the deposition and preservation of the Tertiary ball clays in Devon.

Clay cutting by hand around 1900.
Photo courtesy of Watts Blake Bearne & Co. Plc.

DERIVATION AND DEPOSITION OF THE BALL CLAYS

The climate in the lower Tertiary period, in what is today South West England, was sub-tropical. The very warm, wet conditions resulted in a deep weathering mantle on the Carboniferous and Devonian slates and the granite uplands. The feldspar minerals within the granite were changed to a moderately ordered kaolinite. Sediments derived from the erosion of the thick weathering mantle were channelled into this valley by rivers. The coarser sands and gravels formed alluvial sheets or fans on the valley floor and the clay, slit and vegetation were deposited in shallow lakes. Large rafts of vegetation debris accumulated in the swamp-like lakes. Occasional drier interludes allowed the lakes to dry out and vegetation to spread across the exposed mudflats. These drier periods can be recognised by the presence of rootlet horizons and slit filled sun-cracks in the ball clay seams.

A Bovey Basin gravity survey recorded a maximum depth in excess of 1300 metres. The Basin extends for approximately 11km north-west - south-east and 6km in an east-west direction.

Ball clay is extracted predominantly from opencast workings. However, a small quantity of high quality clay is still extracted from underground mines in cases where surface access is impracticable and where higher production costs can be justified through exploration of quantity reserves. Nevertheless, as a result of economic considerations, the role of underground mining will continue to diminish.

Shaft mining of ball clay began around 1870 and involved sinking vertical shafts to a maximum legal and practical depth of 50 metres. This method was used up until about 1960 and was subsequently replaced by inclined shafts, known locally as adits, which allowed access to underground mines.

In opencast working, the exposed clay is won mechanically by means of hydraulic excavators, then loaded into dumpers and transported to the storage bays.

Throughout the extraction process the type and quality of the clay is monitored by Quarry Operators, in co-operation with the Works Quality Control Laboratory.

Although most of the ball clay sold to the European ceramic industries is supplied in shredded form, considerable quantities are sold in pulverised air-floated form to other industries, as well as to ceramic producers in more distant locations. In certain cases for specialised uses, the clay may also have some additional form of chemical modification or treatment. The majority of the clay processed in this manner is sold in bagged, palletised form, but for deliveries within the United Kingdom, bulk transport by road tanker can be used.

Exports of ball clay to Northern Europe and the Mediterranean are made from the local port of Teignmouth. Approximately 220,000 tonnes of ball clay are exported annually through this port. Exports to more distant countries are made through the deep water ports of Liverpool, Southampton, Ipswich and Felixstowe.

THE TRANSPORTATION OF CLAY IN THE 19TH CENTURY

After its preparation at the works, the clay was loaded into barges on the nearby Stover Canal for movement to Teignmouth to be transferred to larger vessels. The canal barges used a Viking type sail for their progress to the port. They were attended by the lightermen, who possibly lived in the derelict cottages close to the long bypass river bridge west of the Passage House Inn, Kingsteignton. Each lighter carried approximately 50 tons per load. The amount shipped per annum averaged 20,000 tons (Lysons 1822). These men used flat-bottomed boats to load or unload ships in the docks or elsewhere. They were under licence after their apprenticeship and examination by the Watermen and Lightermen Company, incorporated in 1827. Modern transport involves the use of six and eight-wheel tipping lorries plying between the clay works and the ships at Teignmouth Docks.

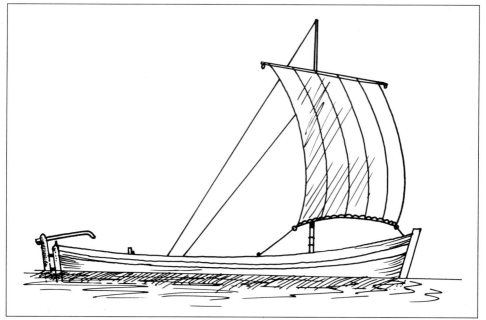

Artist's impression of Clay barge with Viking sail.

COMMON CLAY

In an area of hilly ground, the presence of a spring of water usually denotes the existence of a clay bed. Rain falling on the higher slope permeates the soil as far as the clay area, here it follows gravity and reaches the surface above the non-porous materials, reeds grow and the ground becomes sodden with moisture. On level fields a bed of clay with a light covering of soil is referred to as 'heavy' by the farmer. Beds of clay are common but not always extensive. Engineers who built the dams for the Torquay reservoir complex which straddles the boundaries of three parishes, Bridford, Christow and Hennock used clay from three pits all within a distance of 2½ miles, the farthest being approximately 150 yards north-west of Court Barton farmhouse, the next about the same distance south-east of Elmsley House and the other much nearer at Heckland farm. This pit was used by the St. Thomas Rural District Council as a refuse tip until 1970, its size being 120ft. long, 50 ft. wide and 25ft. deep. Carters were paid 1½d per butt cart load delivered to the dams in the last century.

Clay cellars on the Stover Canel.

THE CURRENT VIEW FROM THE DARTMOOR NATIONAL PARK

(Submitted by Peter White, Deputy National Park Officer).

Previous chapters have described the legacy of history and interest left by mineral extraction in the valley over many generations and the importance of the industry to the local economy. They also hint at the impact on the landscape, and the levels of pollution created.

In recent years the market for many minerals has changed, and sites in the valley have closed down as a result. Public awareness of conservation issues has at the same time been growing. The Dartmoor landscape is now valued as a national asset, recognised in its designation as a National Park. Pollution levels which were once commonplace are no longer tolerated, and the traffic generated by mineral working is regarded as a burden on local roads. On the other hand derelict mine and quarry sites have in many cases acquired a value as part of our industrial history, as valued habitats, or as sites of geological interest and there may still be a demand for certain minerals to meet local, regional or national needs. So what view does the National Park Authority take of the relics from the past, and of potential proposals for the future?

All new mineral working proposals now require a planning permission, and as the local planning authority the NPA takes the view that the environment of the Teign Valley should not be prejudiced by new workings unless there is a clear benefit to the area. Thus a proposal to work a site in a different and less damaging way to that already permitted may prove acceptable, and walling may indeed be necessary if the character of the buildings and landscape of the area is to be preserved. Very occasionally, there may be an overriding national need for a mineral to be extracted within the National Park, but in such cases the onus must be on the developer to prove the point.

In the same way that damaging new developments should be resisted, sites which are currently inactive, but where re-opening could cause problems, should ideally have any outstanding planning permissions rescinded. This has been done, by means of Prohibition Orders, at Scattor Rock Quarry, Christow, and at Great Rock Mine, Hennock. An Order has also been served on Blackingstone Quarry at Bridford, and the outcome of a public inquiry is awaited. The confirmation of an Order does not preclude a future application for working (which could be permitted if considered beneficial) but it does give NPA control over the situation. It is also possible to make Orders requiring the landscaping and tidying up of disused sites, but the view has been taken that in most cases nature has effectively recolonised, and created an attractive and valuable habitat, and that the remains of old machinery, tramways and buildings have a value as history, and are seen as items of interest rather than eyesores. Many sites are also best left undisturbed from a pollution point of view. The waste tips at Wheal Exmouth or Bridford Barytes no longer cause significant pollution because weathering processes have removed toxic minerals from the surface layers, but any disturbance of these layers could have disastrous consequences for the River Teign.

Thus the emphasis is now on conserving the remains of the past, so that both local people and visitors can enjoy them. This may be achieved by simply doing nothing, or it may require positive action. Thus planning permission to convert the ruinous engine house at Wheal Exmouth into a house was granted on the basis that permitting the new use will ensure survival of this important building and the permission also requires maintenance of other historic structures - principally the chimneys. On other structures direct NPA conservation work may be needed, as is planned for the chimney at Birch Mine, Bridford.

Adding to our knowledge of the past is also important. It has led, for instance, to accurate recording of the remains of lime kilns and quarrymen's cottages at Blackaller Quarry, Drewsteignton; and to the recording on tape of conversations with some of the miners who worked in Great Rock Mine at Hennock.

The Teign Valley has a unique history, which has created a unique environment. Protection of all of the elements of that environment is now the priority, but it must be done in a way which does not stifle all development and change.

ACKNOWLEDGEMENTS

The author wishes to thank the following for their help so freely given whilst researching the contents of this book.

Castle Drogo.
The Devonshire Association.
Christow Parish Council.
Camborne School of Mines.
The Devon County Minerals Office.
Express & Echo Publications.
Watts Blake Bearne & Co. Plc.
Mrs S. Douthwaite.
Mrs T. Walker. (DNP Research Officer).
Mrs A. Benewith.
Mrs E. Hocking. (Bridford Barytes Mine).
M. Stuart. (Bridford Barytes Mine).
V. Lauren. (Blackingstone Quarry).
R. Chudley. (Black Aller Quarry).
N. Kingdom. (Aller Mine).
N. Tuckett. (Bennah & Aller Mines).
J. Major. (Scatter Rock Quarry).
C. Smale. (Scatter Rock Quarry).
C. Burgess. (Christow Station & Scatter Rock Quarry).
M. Steer. (Birch Ellers Mine).
R. Thatcher. (Ryecroft Quarry).
A. Ball. (Hennock).
R. Baber. (Reed Mine).
P. Hughes. (Crockham Quarry).
The Late S. Bishop. (Crockham Quarry).
T. Wright. (Wheal Exmouth).
Lord Exmouth.
E. Lee. (Chudleigh District).
T. Shears. (Palace Quarry, Chudleigh).
K. Adams. (Grealy Quarry).

BIBLIOGRAPHY

Lysons Book on Mining.	1821.
Hunts Mineral Statistics.	1877.
The Records of Samuel & Wilfred Clark.	1859-1873.

NOTES